THIS INFANT 1

A Christmas Cantata
Music, Words and Narration by Richard Hepburn

'to my children Jamie and Colette'

Arranged by ALISON HEDGER for piano,
voice with optional second parts and
two recorders. Guitar chords are given.
The addition of a rhythm section will
be at the teacher's discretion.

N.B. ALL SECOND PARTS ARE OPTIONAL

1.	A Little Child Was Born	Unison with Chorus in Two Parts
2.	The Time Is Right	Two Parts
3.	Mary And Joseph	Unison, Two Parts and Solo
4.	Herod's Song	Solo with Unison Chorus
5.	Song Of The Angels And Shepherds	Unison with Chorus in Two Parts
6.	Innkeeper's Song	Solo, Recorder Duet with Unison Chorus
7.	Song Of The Wise Men	Two Parts
8.	Jesus Christ Was Born This Happy Day	Unison

For concert use (approximately 25 minutes) and for use in
conjunction with the traditional Nativity tableau and mime.
Suitable for Juniors, Middle Schools and Lower Secondary –
but this essentially singable music will also appeal to Infants
and adult groups.

The carols will also prove useful taken out of context, as
they are complete on their own, and so can be used in any
Christmas programme.

3 SOLOISTS	–	MARY in No. 3
		HEROD in No. 4
		INNKEEPER in No. 6
RECORDER DUET –		in No. 6

ISBN 1-8709-9703-4
Order No: GA 10091

"The piano accompaniments reflect the differing moods of each of the carols. Several pedal marks have been included where I think they will help the less able pianist. The second vocal parts are not essential. The Cantata is meant for the smallest and simplest groups to sing – and will be just as delightful sung in unison."

1.
A Little Child Was Born
CHORUS IN TWO PARTS

♩ = 160 With simplicity and a gentle rocking movement

lit - tle child was born, in Beth - le - hem to - day.
moth - er Ma - ry, dear, she rocks her lit - tle child.

I heard it from the shep - herds down our way. He's
Ga - zes on His face so peace - ful, calm and mild. And

NARRATOR: Our story starts almost 2000 years ago.
It is the best known story in the world and has
been told in countless different ways. The Romans
are in occupation. The Jewish nation has been eagerly
awaiting some sign of the arrival of the Messiah;
the new King. The scene is set. The time is right.

2.
The Time Is Right
TWO PARTS

NARRATOR: And so it was, just as the angel had said to Mary.
Shortly before her baby was due, she and Joseph received instructions
to complete a census. In order to do this they had to travel to Bethlehem.

3.
Mary And Joseph

UNISON, TWO PARTS AND SOLO

Ev'-ry step seems to get hard-er. We must find a wel-com-ing door.

ALL Ev'-ry step seems to get hard-er.

We must find a wel-com-ing door.

NARRATOR: We now change our scene to the palace of King Herod,
a governor of the Jews appointed by the Romans to keep order.
He has recently heard rumours of a new Jewish king.
Things were getting desperate.

4.
Herod's Song

SOLO AND UNISON CHORUS

1. Things are get - ting des - p'rate. ___ Don't they know I'm
3. Send me my per - son - al ar - my. ___ Ral - ly to the

boss? ___ Ig - nore these fan - cy ru - mours, ___ Or
call. ___ Child - ren un - der two years, ___ You'll

SOLO

bet - ter be   on   the   safe   side. ___   A   king; that means a
just can't take an-y   chan - ces. ___   I   don't be - lieve it's

Dm   E   A7   Dm

boy. ___ ___ ___   A Child-ren are go - ing to   suf - fer. ___   —
true. ___ ___   A man   in my pos - it - ion, ___   Well,

E   A7   Dm   E   A7

CHORUS
f

That will   be   my   ploy.   They say a new king's been
what else can I   do?

D   G

born.____ How ri - dic - u - lous can you get? Well

I've got a trick or two up— my sleeve, 'Cause I'm not fin-ished ____ yet!

First time

Second time

I'm not fin-ished, ____ I'm not fin -ished ____ yet!

glissando

ff

NARRATOR: On the hillside far above Bethlehem, a group
of shepherds were watching their sheep by moonlight.
They were sleepy, hungry and huddled up tight
against the cold, when suddenly...

© *Golden Apple Productions 1987 – "This Infant Boy"*

5.
Song Of The Angels And Shepherds

CHORUS IN TWO PARTS

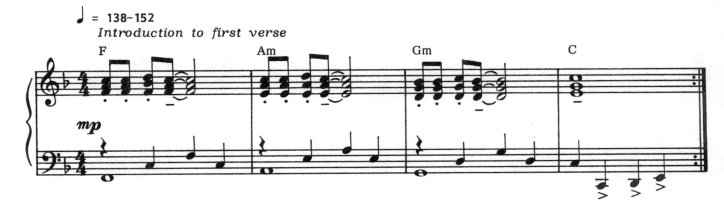

1. The light in the dark night Shone down from the sky.
2. The shep-herds were speech-less, They looked for the star.

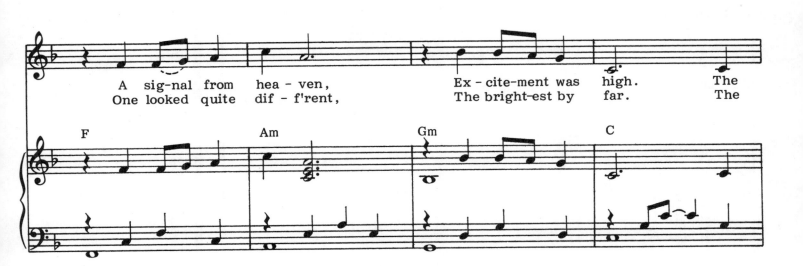

A sig-nal from hea - ven, Ex - cite-ment was high. The
One looked quite dif - f'rent, The bright-est by far. The

18

shep - herds were ner - vous, Knew not what to do,
an - gels must be right. The mean - ing was clear.

We are God's an - gels, We've good news for you.
Let's do as they tell us, What good have we to fear?

CHORUS to verse one

I
Fol - low the bright star to Beth - le - hem's plain.

II
Fol - low the bright star to Beth - le - hem's plain.

NARRATOR: Like Joseph and Mary, all the people born
in Bethlehem had been ordered to return.
The town was overflowing with visitors.
Joseph and Mary found it difficult to find
anywhere to stay. The innkeeper's
rejections were all too familiar.

© *Golden Apple Productions 1987 – "This Infant Boy"*

6.
Innkeeper's Song

SOLO, TWO RECORDERS, UNISON CHORUS

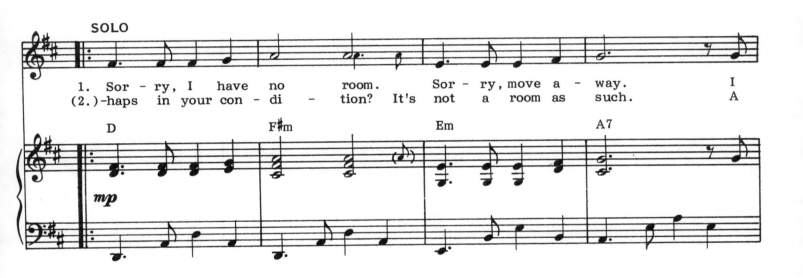

1. Sor - ry, I have no room. Sor - ry, move a - way. I
(2.)-haps in your con - di - tion? It's not a room as such. A

would have liked to help you. Per - haps an - oth - er day.
sta - ble I can of - fer, I know it is - n't much.

ALL - recorder descant melody

3. In a dark-ened sta - ble Ma - ry bore her Son.

2. Per-

SOLO

continue in octaves to finish

Jo - seph there to help her. Ox and ass looked on.

Je - sus, ba - by Je - sus, There for all to see._____

Ly - ing in a man - ger, Sleep-ing si - lent - ly.

NARRATOR: And so in these simple surroundings was born
the baby who was to change the world.
Wise men, who had been following signs from
the stars, arrived to pay their tribute to
the new King . . . . . The King of the world.

7.
Song Of The Wise Men

TWO PARTS

1. Wise men bring-ing gifts, we come from a - far.

We've been guid-ed by the bright-est star.

Now our quest is ov - er. Jour-ney stops right here.

28

© *Golden Apple Productions 1987 – "This Infant Boy"*

NARRATOR: Although our story happened all that
time ago, we can still today join with
the shepherds, angels and kings and
celebrate together the very first Christmas.

8.
Jesus Christ Was Born This Happy Day

UNISON

♩ = 120–138

1. Je - sus Christ was born this hap-py day, _____
2. Wise men came from East-ern lands a - far, _____
3. Though this hap-pened ma - ny years a - go, _____

Born in Beth - le - hem so far a - way. _____
Guid - ed through the night by one bright star. _____
We can still tell Him we love Him so. _____

Shep - herds left their flocks and came a - long.
Worn and wea - ry still they came a - long.
Sing His prai - ses as we go a - long.

Came to praise Him with a hap - py song.
Came to praise Him with a hap - py song.
Come to praise Him with a hap - py song.

CHORUS

Glo - ry, glo - ry to this In - fant boy,

Come to earth to bring us peace and joy.

Let the bells ring out on Christ-mas morn,

1st & 2nd time

Tell the world that Je - sus Christ is born.

last time

rit. born to - day.

8ve L.H. over

10/99(35283)
Printed in England